Felix

LECOUPPEY

L'AGILITÉ
Twenty-Five Progressive Studies

Opus 20

FOR PIANO

K 03608

L'Agilité.
Twenty-five Progressive Studies.

FELIX LECOUPPEY. Op. 20.

Allegro. (♩ = 138)

Printed in the U. S. A.

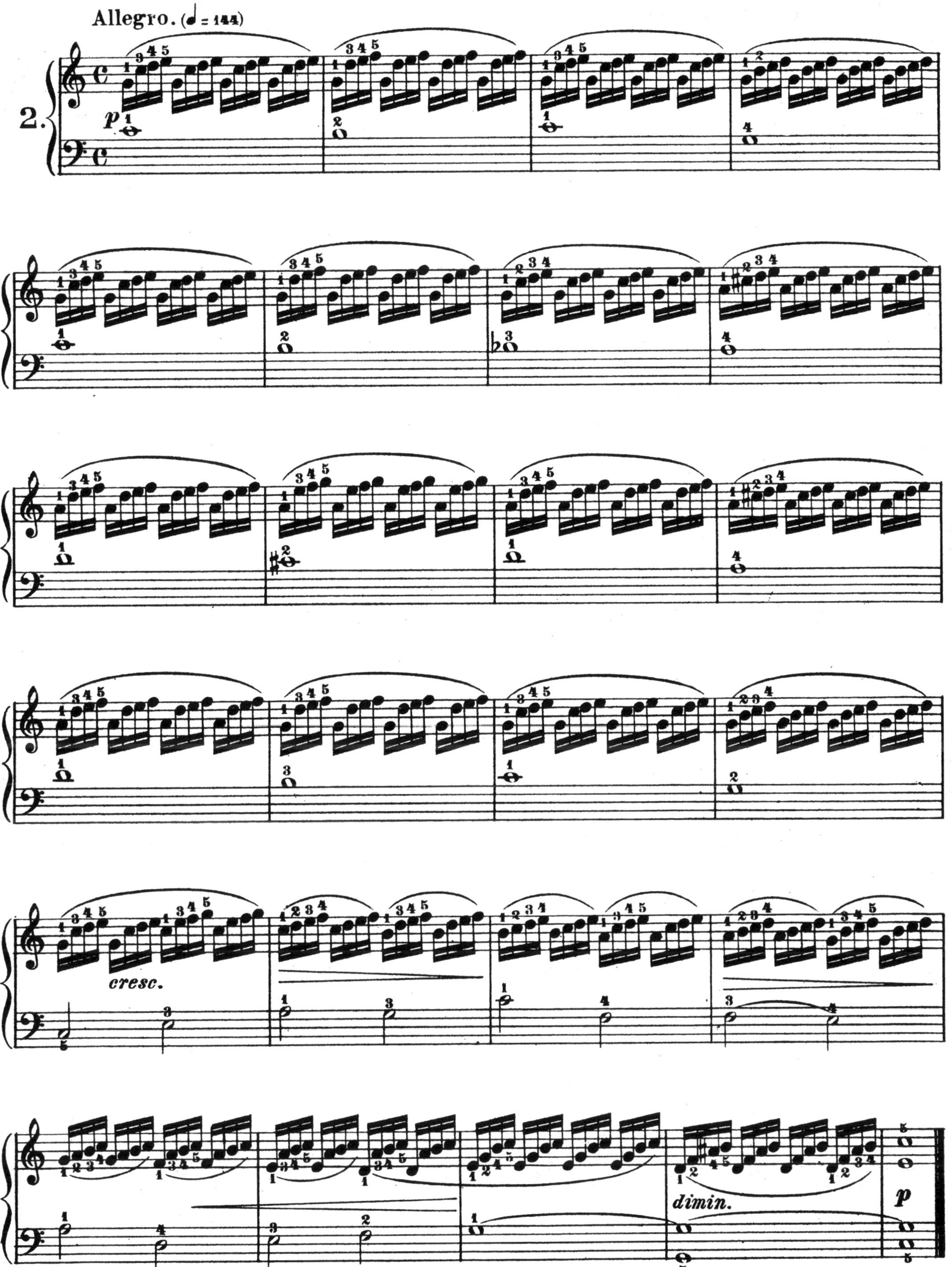
Allegro. (♩ = 144)
2.
p
cresc.
dimin.
p

Allegro moderato. (♩=120)
3.
p
cresc.
ff
mf
p delicato

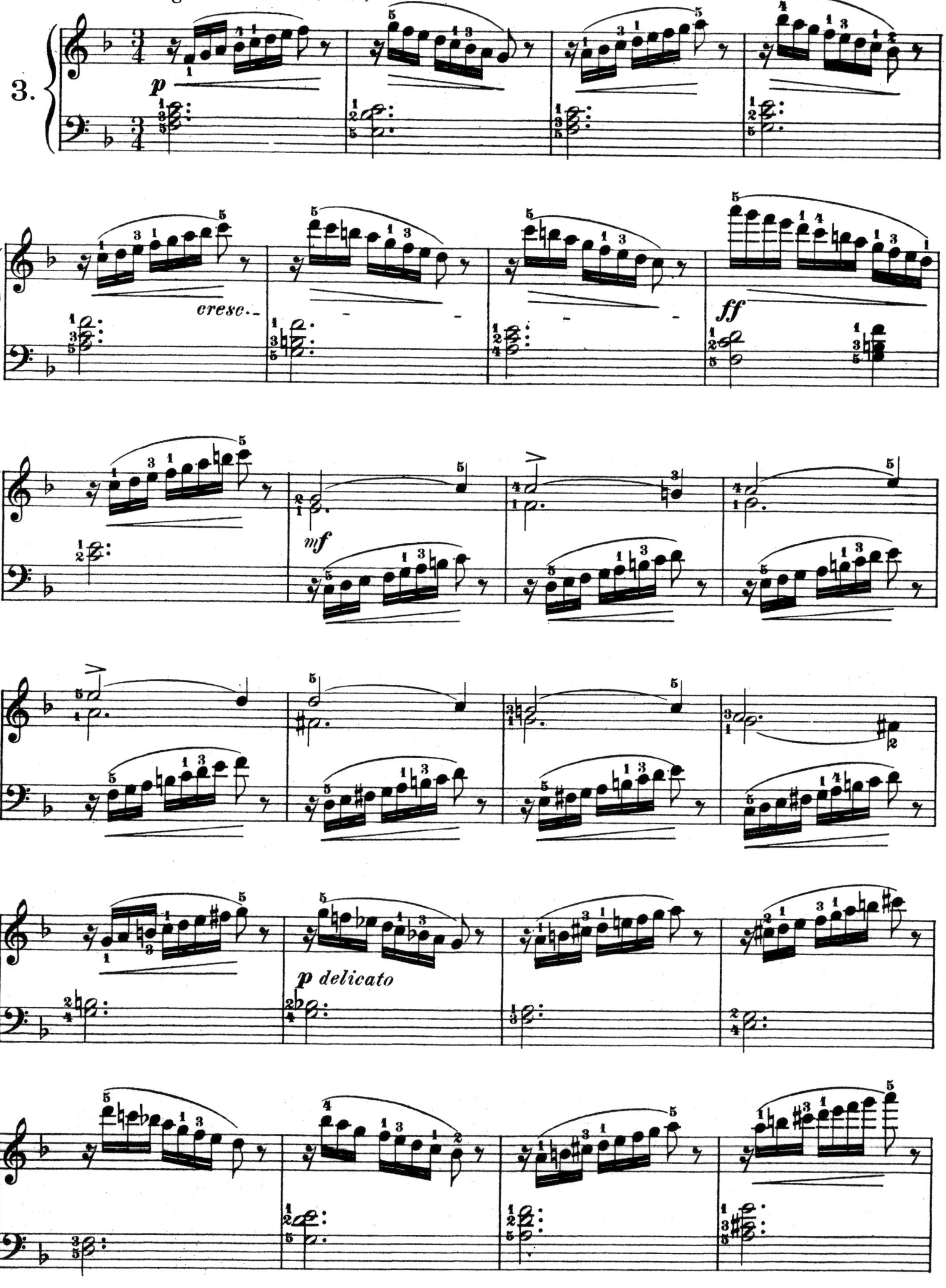

Allegro moderato. (♩=126)
4.
p leggiero
mf
p
dim.
poco riten.
sf
p

Allegretto. (♩=112)
5.
p
mf
cresc. —
f
p
cresc. —
f

Allegro. (♩ = 138)
6.
p leggiero
sempre p
cresc.

9
f
dolce.
sf
p
cresc.
ff

10
Allegretto. (♪ = 50.)
7.
p
3 3 3
3 2 1 3 2 1 3 2 1
3 2 1 3 2 1 3 2 1
3 2 1 3 2 1 3 2 1
3 2 1 3
p
dim.
mf
più f
p
sf
p
p
sf
p
sf

a tempo
dim. e riten.
p
più f
p
dim.
f
p
pp e riten.

Allegro. (♩ = 152.)
8.
f
f
mf
f
f

Allegro moderato. (♩ = 100.)

9.

Allegro. (♩ = 144.)
10.
f
f
mf
f

Allegretto. (♩.=88)

11.

ff
p
p
f
p
p
pp   e rall.

12.
Allegro.(♩ = 144.)
mf
cresc.
f
fp
fp
fp
p

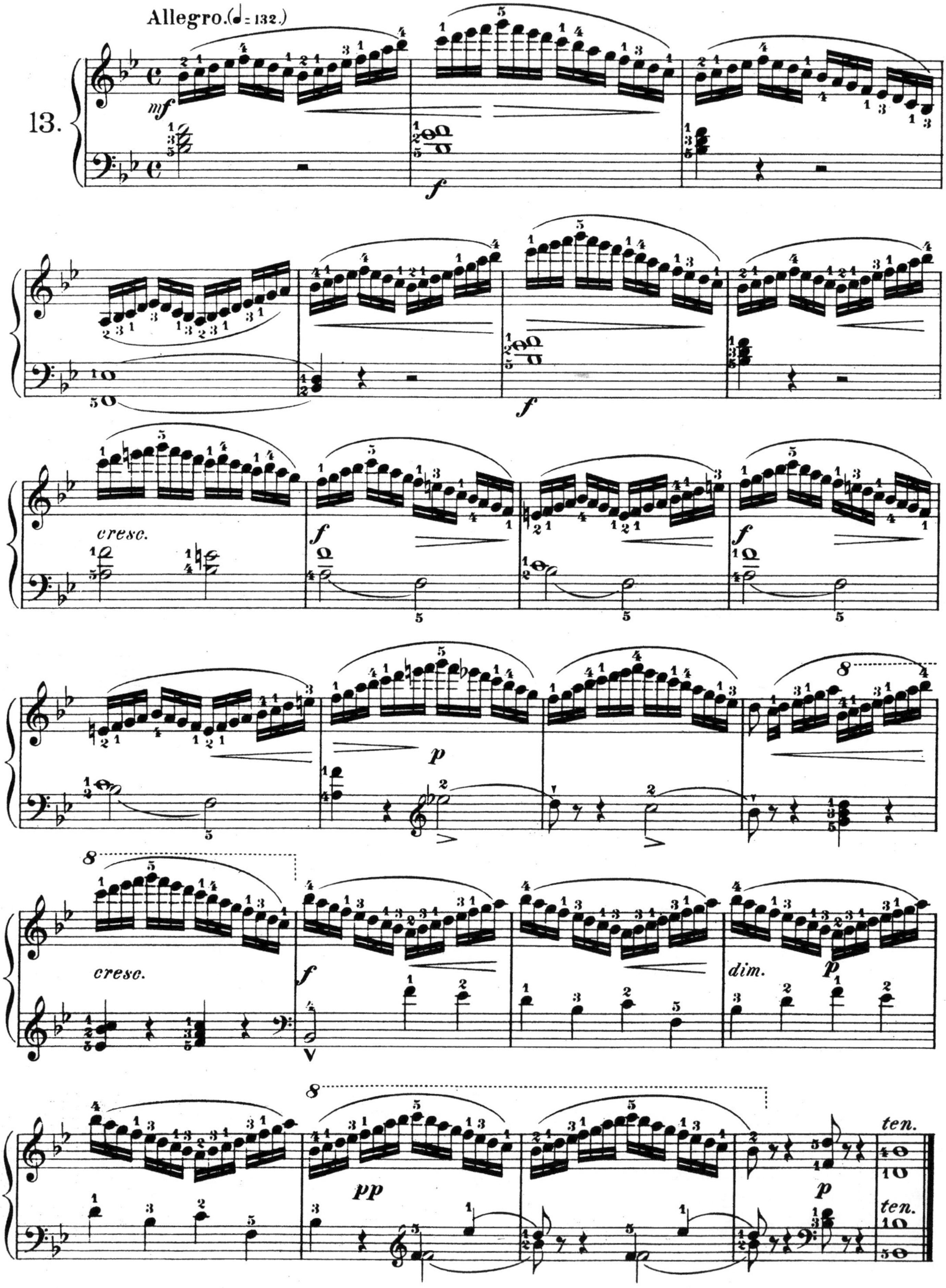

Allegro.(♩=132.)
13.
mf
f
f
cresc.
f
f
f
p
cresc.
f
dim.
p
V
pp
p
ten.
ten.

14.
Allegro.(♩.=50.)
p
mf
f
8
8
8
f

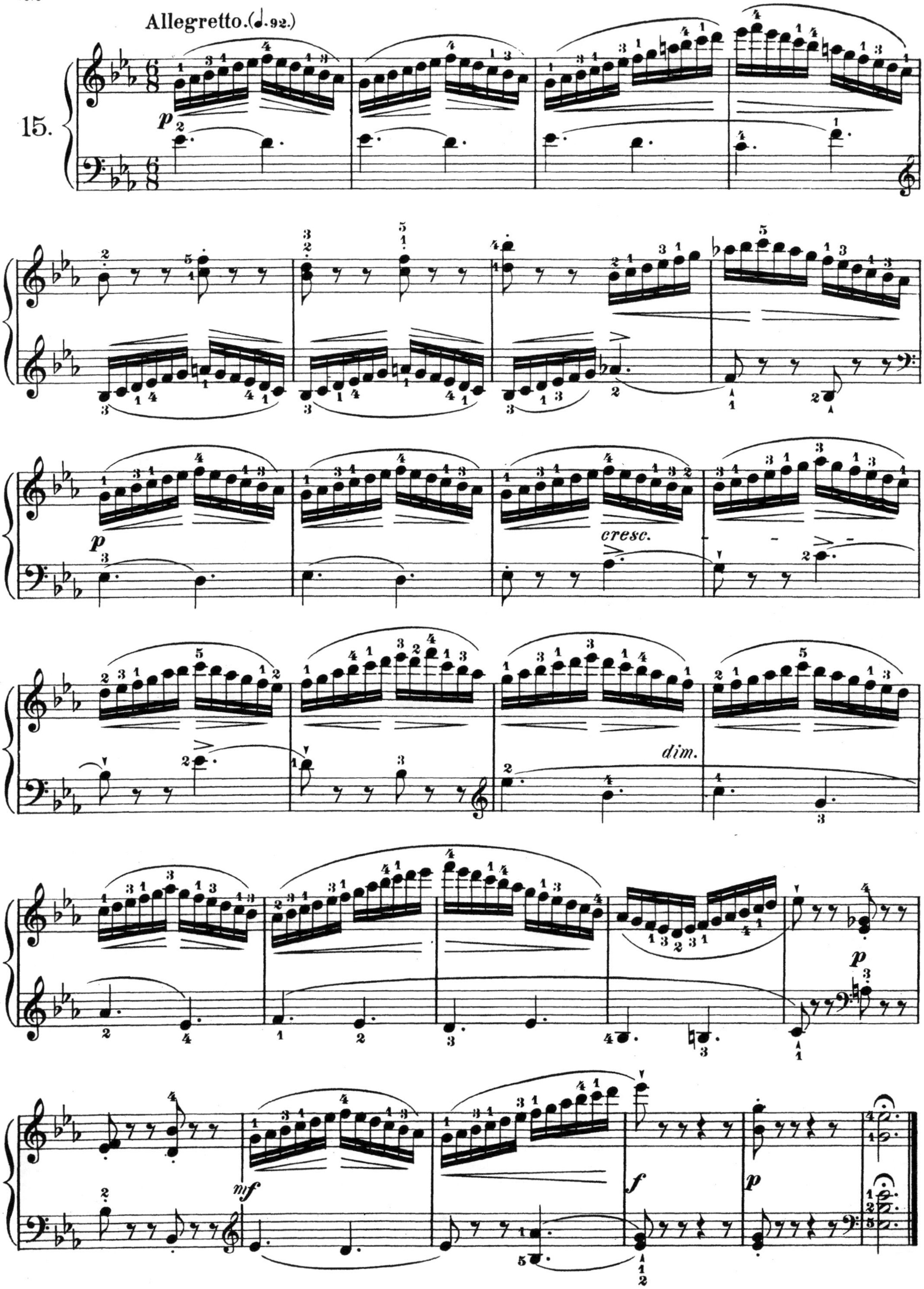

Allegretto. (♩.=92.)
15.
p
cresc.
dim.
mf
f
p

Allegro. (♩ = 152)
16.
p leggiero
mf
p
pp dimin.

Allegro (♩ = 126)
17.
mf
più f
p
più f
p

Allegro (= 80)
18.
p leggiero
cresc.
f
più f

Allegro (♩=138)
19.
mf
cresc.
mf
cresc.
f
p
f

20.
Allegro moderato. (♩=120)
p
cresc.
p
cresc.
p
f

Allegro. (♩=69)
21.
pp leggiero
sempre p
f

22.
Allegro. (♩=160)
p leggiero
più f
p
f
mf

f
p
p
p leggiero
p

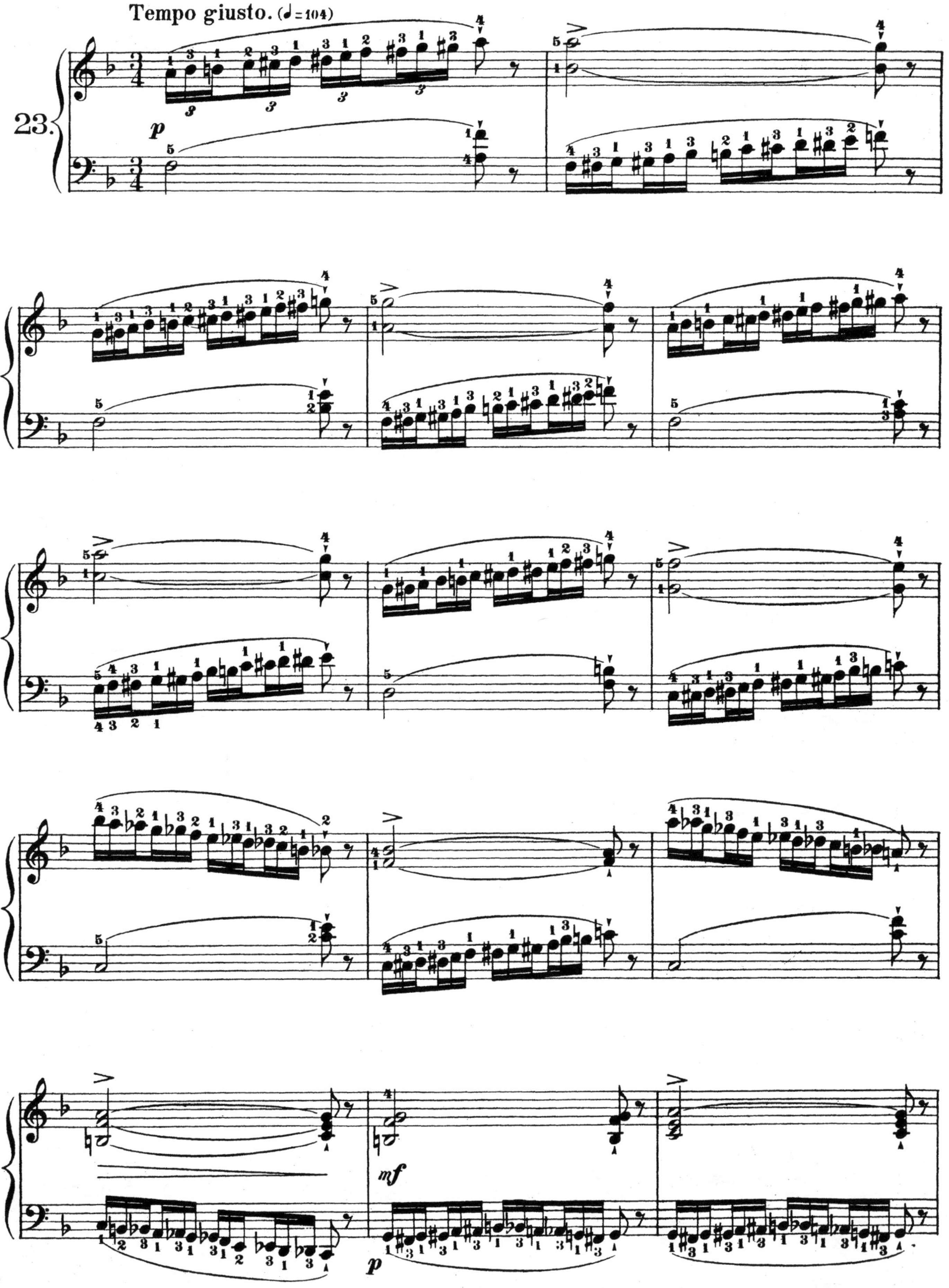
Tempo giusto. (♩=104)
23.
p
mf
p

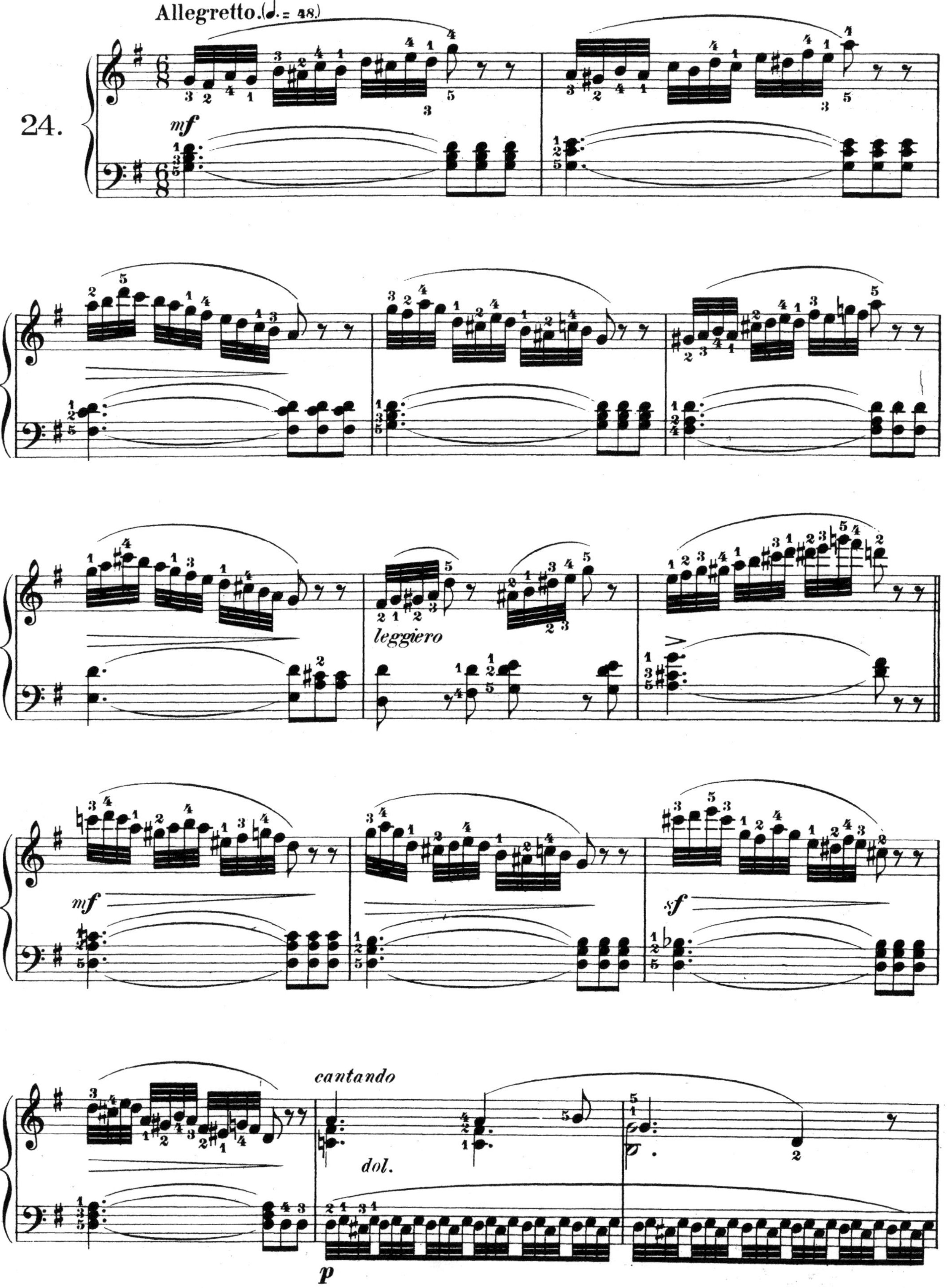
Allegretto. (♩. = 48.)
24.
mf
mf
leggiero
mf
sf
cantando
dol.
p
p

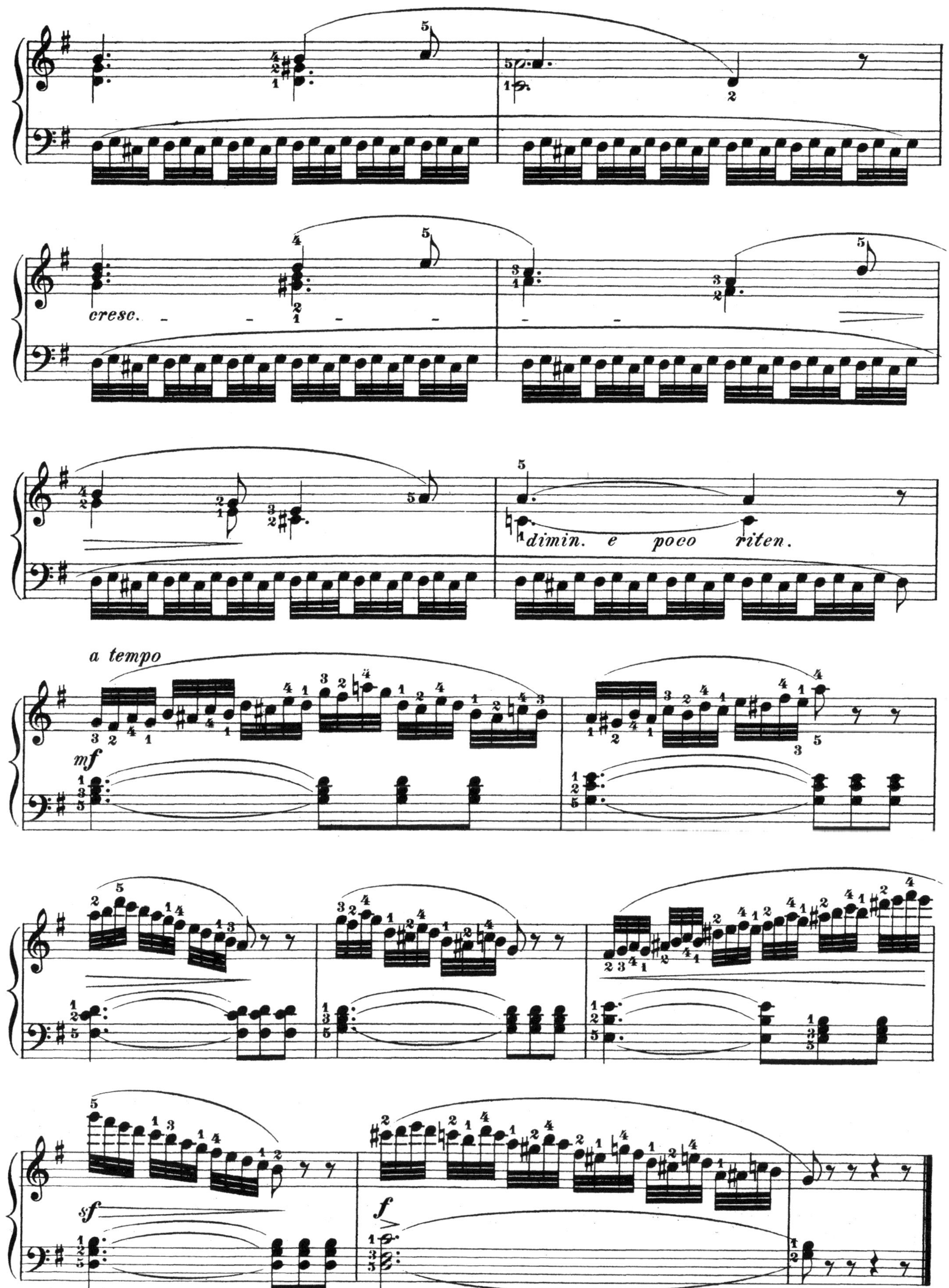

cresc.
dimin. e poco riten.
a tempo
mf
sf
f

Allegretto.(♩ = 116.)
25.
p

p
cresc.
8
8
3
3
cresc.
5 4 4 5 5 4 4 5
f
V
5
5
5
dimin. e rall.
pp